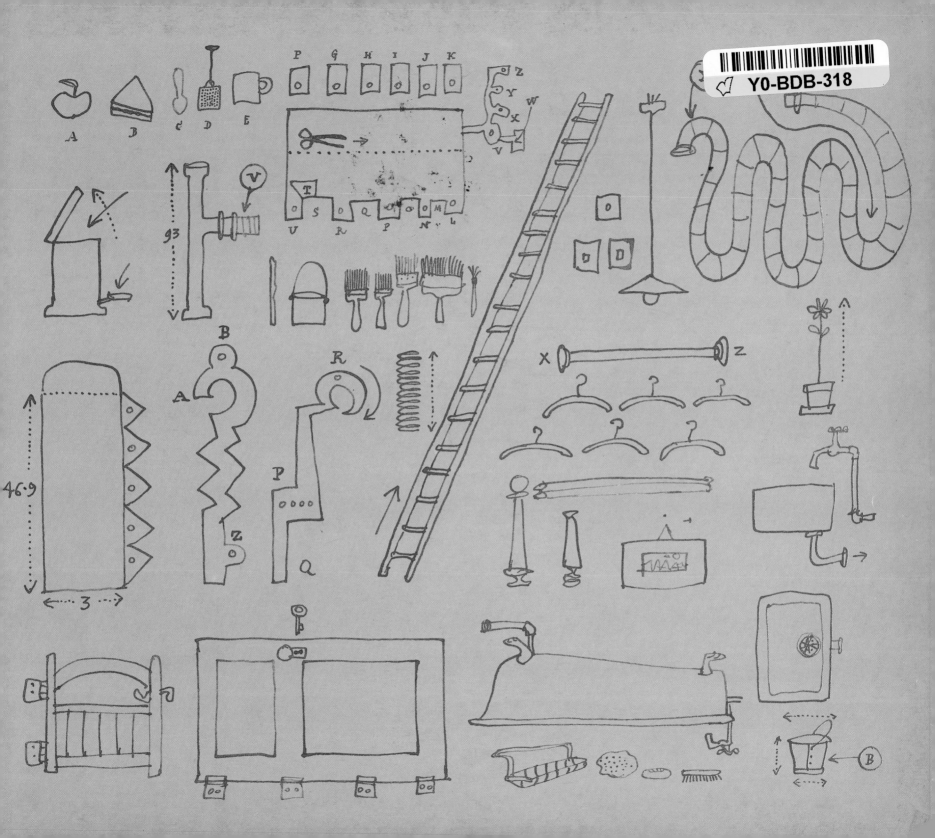

First published in Great Britain 1994 by Hamish Hamilton Ltd., London

Atheneum Books for Young Readers
An imprint of Simon & Schuster Children's Publishing Division
1230 Avenue of the Americas
New York, NY 10020

The text of this book is set in 24 pt. CG Collage Bold.
The illustrations were done in watercolors.

Printed in Italy by L.E.G.O.

10   9   8   7   6   5   4   3   2   1

ISBN 0-689-80006-1

Library of Congress Catalog Card Number: 94-72452

John Yeoman and Quentin Blake

The DO-IT-YOURSELF House that Jack Built

Atheneum Books for Young Readers

This is the house that Jack built.

This is the malt
    that lay in the house
        that Jack built.

Twenty sacks of malt, Jack. Sign here, please.
But I don't remember ordering any malt. There must be some mistake. I'm building a house.
Whoopee. Lunch for life!

This is the rat
    that ate the malt
        that lay in the house
            that Jack built.

This is the cat
  that killed the rat
    that ate the malt
      that lay in the house
        that Jack built.

This is the dog
   that worried the cat
      that killed the rat
         that ate the malt
            that lay in the house
               that Jack built.

This is the cow with the crumpled horn
that tossed the dog
that worried the cat
that killed the rat
that ate the malt
that lay in the house
that Jack built.

This is the maiden all forlorn
    that milked the cow with the crumpled horn
        that tossed the dog
            that worried the cat
                that killed the rat
                    that ate the malt
                        that lay in the house
                            that Jack built.

This is the man all tattered and torn
that kissed the maiden all forlorn
that milked the cow with the crumpled horn
that tossed the dog
that worried the cat
that killed the rat
that ate the malt
that lay in the house
that Jack built.

He's luckier than I was.
Well, we only have to find out where this goes and we're nearly finished.
All right. If I can have a go with the power-drill.
My angel! Will you marry me?
Anyway, I might as well paint it red.
Nicely crumpled.
More trouble.

This is the priest all shaven and shorn
that married the man all tattered and torn
that kissed the maiden all forlorn
that milked the cow with the crumpled horn
that tossed the dog
that worried the cat
that killed the rat
that ate the malt
that lay in the house
that Jack built.

This is the cock that crowed in the morn
that waked the priest all shaven and shorn
that married the man all tattered and torn
that kissed the maiden all forlorn
that milked the cow with the crumpled horn
that tossed the dog
that worried the cat
that killed the rat
that ate the malt
that lay in the house
that Jack built.

This is the farmer sowing his corn
   that kept the cock that crowed in the morn
     that waked the priest all shaven and shorn
      that married the man all tattered and torn
       that kissed the maiden all forlorn
         that milked the cow with the crumpled horn
        that tossed the dog
         that worried the cat
         that killed the rat
          that ate the malt
           that lay in the house
            that Jack built.

This is the house that Jack built.

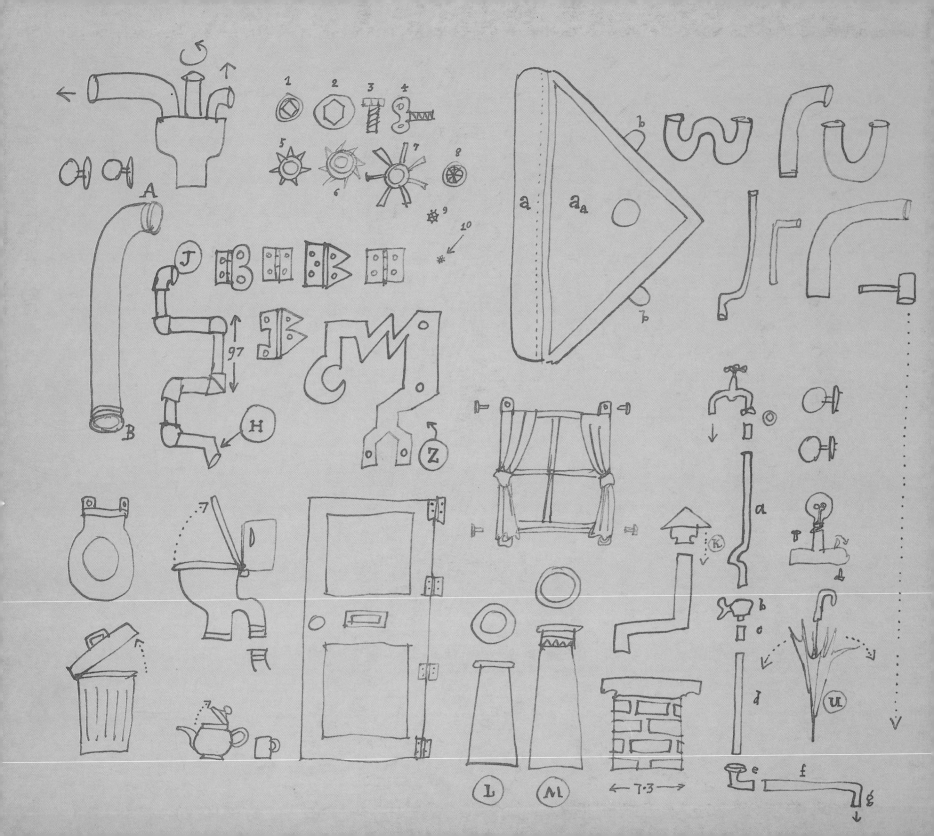